# The
# Gratitude
# Journal

# The Gratitude Journal

## Create words and images on a thankful path to daily joy

### Lisa Dyer

ARCTURUS

All images are courtesy of Shutterstock

ARCTURUS

This edition published in 2022 by Arcturus Publishing Limited
26/27 Bickels Yard, 151–153 Bermondsey Street,
London SE1 3HA

ISBN: 978-1-3988-0889-8
AD008823US

Printed in China

# CONTENTS

"Imagination is the beginning of creation. You imagine what you desire, you will what you imagine, and at last, you create what you will."

GEORGE BERNARD SHAW

*"Gratitude can transform common days into thanksgivings, turn routine jobs into joy and change ordinary opportunities into blessings."*

WILLIAM ARTHUR WARD

# GETTING STARTED

Welcome to your gratitude journal, where you will reflect on and record all the wonderful things in your life. Designed to cultivate and reinforce a positive mental attitude through drawing and coloring prompts, this activity journal will help you express gratitude through creativity.

Using a range of art techniques, the exercises draw on memories, life experiences, self-exploration, imagination, and observations. Noticing the world and its beauty, whether it is a bird in your garden, a starry night, or a fabulous scarf a neighbor is wearing will help you become more appreciative of the people, places, and experiences that give meaning to your life, and look to the future with hope and optimism.

Organized by themes, the chapters encourage you to explore color, shape, and pattern, as well as linework, perspective, and landscape. Whether you are a complete novice, an avid doodler, or a skilled artist, the activities will unlock your creative potential and help you focus on what really matters and makes you happy.

## Tools and Materials

There are many mark-making tools to choose from, all with their own special qualities. You will have your favorites! If you are just beginning your art journey, start with something familiar, such as colored pencils or markers, and then expand your collection.

PENCILS  Lead (graphite) pencils are available in a variety of hardnesses, from a 9H, which creates sharp lines, to a soft 2B, perfect for blending and shading.

COLORED PENCILS  Easy to use and mess-free, they can be used to build up the depth of color and colors can be layered over each other. Water-soluble versions can be blended with a damp brush or a cotton swab dipped in baby oil. There is every color imaginable, though it is always useful to have a wide variety of neutrals, especially for skin tones and animals.

CHINA MARKERS  These wax pencils are available in a limited range of colors. Use the white version for adding highlight details and drawing on black paper.

PENS  A fine-tip black pen is excellent for adding detail, outlining, and sketching, as well as hatching, stippling, and other techniques. There are also gel pens in vibrant colors, metallic, and white, as well as felt-tipped markers in various thicknesses.

BRUSH PENS  With a brush tip, these are water-based and give a watercolor effect. They can be used for line-making as well as blending and layering washes of color.

CRAYONS  Not just for kids! Crayons can be used to create texture and soft background color, and layered to create more depth of color.

WATERCOLORS  Various palettes are available, but colors are blendable. You can use these with just about any type of brush shape but make sure the brush is wet before you pick up the pigment.

CHARCOALS, CHALKS, AND OIL PASTELS
These are all very smudgeable mediums that can be messy but excellent for blending, shading, and creating soft, colorful illustrations.

# WHEEL OF LIFE

This useful exercise helps you identify areas of your life that perhaps aren't working for you as well as others, and where you need to focus more of your energy and gratitude. Fill in the bars in colors up to your satisfaction level for each area of your life. For example, your social "wedge" might be fully colored in, whereas you might only be able to fill in the first two or three tiers of your self-time.

SELF-TIME

MENTAL

SPIRITUAL

SOCIAL

CAREER

FAMILY

FINANCIAL

PHYSICAL

# I AM GRATEFUL FOR...

List all the things that first spring to mind beginning with each letter.
Choose a different style of lettering for each one.

A

B

C

D

E

F

G

H

I

J

K

L

| | |
|---|---|
| MAdi | Noah |
| O | P |
| Q | R |
| S | T |
| U | V |
| W | X |
| Y | Z |

Chapter 1:

# FAMILY & FRIENDS

*"In ordinary life, we hardly realize that we receive a great deal more than we give, and that it is only with gratitude that life becomes rich."*

DIETRICH BONHOEFFER

The people in your life, both those close to you and those you observe or encounter, are the focus of the activities in this chapter. While you're drawing and imagining, think about their special attributes and features, the ways in which you appreciate them and how you could build more gratitude and kindness into your connections with them.

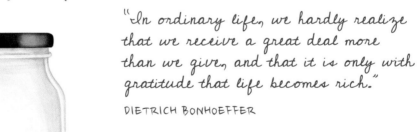

# FAMILY PORTRAITS

Draw the people you are most grateful for in these frames —those who form your core support group, who are with you through thick and thin.

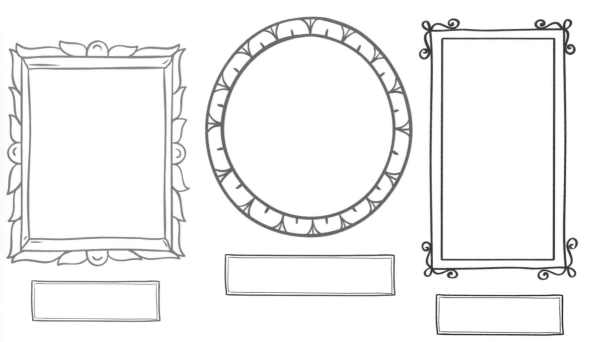

Next, give each one a title for the job they do for you, such as: cheerleader, party organizer, protector, financial advisor, fashion consultant, voice of reason, peacekeeper, or even "shoulder to cry on."

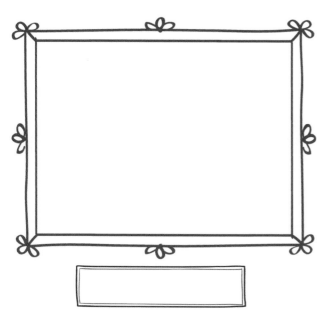

# LOVE HEARTS

Scribble drawings and doodles are fun and
easy enough for a child to do. Start with
basic shapes like the hearts here to remind
you of those you are lucky enough to love and
who love you back. Then try animal shapes,
figures, and faces—the technique can be used
to create sophisticated portraits.

# WHAT'S IN THE JAR?

Draw items to give to someone in these jars—do they contain cookies, jam, sweets, nuts, paperclips, coins, colored pencils? Who are they for?

DRAW IN HAIR STYLES
USING LOOPS OR LINES

# A COMMUNITY OF PEOPLE

Social encounters, whether they are the friends we meet up with, family get-togethers, a neighborhood street party, or just the people we pass every day, help us remember that we are never truly alone. Add details in black pen to make some friends for a gathering or group night out.

DRAW IN
BOOTS OR
SHOES

# DOT FACES

Use black and colored pens or fine-tip markers to make these circles into the faces of people or animals, drawing in hair, ears, and facial features.

# RECEIVED WISDOM

Draw or write down something that you have received from someone else. It could be a good piece of advice, a recommended book, or a skill they taught you, such as how to sew or speak a foreign language.

# SHARED WISDOM

Now draw something you have taught to, or shared with, another.

# SMALL KINDNESSES

Record a kind deed someone did for you today—maybe they held the door open for you, brought you a cup of tea, or offered to empty the dishwasher or take your dog for a walk.

# SMILES AND SURPRISES

Record an event that made you smile today or that surprised you in a good way.

# A FRIENDSHIP TREE

Draw a tree here and let every main branch represent one of your closest friends—add their name or their picture. From each of those branches, add other people they have introduced you to, and so on. You will soon see how wide your circle of friends has grown and how much bigger it can get!

# FRIENDLY CONNECTIONS

Draw faces and clothing on these paper-chain friends. Use colors and details you associate with real-life friends and include nice adjectives about them if you like. Think about how they are connected to you—draw yourself in the paper chain.

# THANKFUL FOR...

What are you most grateful for in your life? Choose a word that you relate to most, such as "health," "beauty," "family," "work," "food," "nature." Design the lettering and incorporate 3D and dropped shadows, stripes, dots, patterns, and banners. Or use the letters in an integrated geometric design as here.

# MOOD COLORS

Color in the circles in shades that you feel correspond to the emotions that arise for each topic below. Are they all tones of one color, contrasting, or complementary colors? What might the opposite emotions and colors be?

CREATIVITY        LOVE        GRATITUDE

HAPPINESS        HOPE        EMPATHY

SATISFACTION        CONFIDENCE        EXCITEMENT

# MEMORIAL WREATHS

Design a memorial wreath for a living person—what would you say about the person and how would you honor them? What flowers would you choose? Start with one of these wreaths and embellish the design or create your own. Draw an image that represents them in the center, or choose an empowering word or a catchphrase they always use.

# A FIELD OF SUNFLOWERS

START WITH LIGHTER COLORS FIRST AND BUILD UP COLOR IN LAYERS

These beautiful flowers symbolize long life, happiness, optimism, and loyalty. Draw a field of sunflowers here in pencil first, then color with wash or brush pen.

# COMMEMORATIVE PLATE

Design the souvenir dinner plate below to honor a special event in your life—it could be a wedding, birthday, or any occasion that marked a milestone for you.

# SPECIAL MOMENTS TILES

Design these wall or floor tiles, making each tile represent a memory that you hold dear –
such as a drawing of your pet, an heirloom, a holiday souvenir, a favorite piece of jewelry, or
the pattern of a sweater that your granny knitted for you.

USE DIFFERENT
TONES OF BLUES FOR
ALL THE TILES, OR
CHOOSE A FAMILY
OF TWO TO THREE
COLORS TO FORM A
VISUALLY CONNECTED
COLLECTION

# SHARING FOOD

Draw the dining table where you share meals with your family or loved ones and make place settings for each of the people who will be there. Is it a special celebration or holiday, such as Thanksgiving or a wedding? Or is it the daily evening meal that means the most? Use elements that reflect the occasion and season.

SKETCH IN PENCIL
FIRST, MARKING
OUT AREAS OF
HIGHLIGHTS

START WITH
THE LIGHTEST
WASHES OF
COLOR BEFORE
ADDING DARKER
TONES

# COOKING TOGETHER

Who taught you how to cook, or shared a
secret recipe? What went in the pot?
Remember a happy experience of cooking with
someone here and draw the ingredients and
utensils you used to make it.

# CONTINUOUS LINE PORTRAITS

Every person is unique and interesting. Study the faces of people around you to appreciate the small details that give them character. Note the tilt of head, expression, or dominant features, then draw a portrait using a continuous, unbroken line.

Love ∞

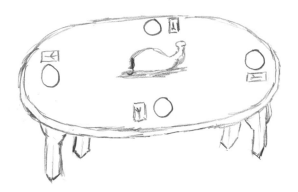

# FAMILIES

What does the word "family" mean to you? What do you appreciate about your family?
Draw a family here—it doesn't have to be your own.

# OBSERVATIONS

What makes someone stand out from the pack? Look at a person you live with or see regularly. Do they favor pink dresses or striped shirts, or perhaps their hair is styled in a distinctive way or they always wear a hat? Capture an image that you associate with them.

Now watch how they
stand and move. Try to
capture their posture
or movement using just
a few strokes of your
brush or marker.

Chapter 2:

# HOME & DAILY LIFE

"Let us rise up and be thankful, for if we didn't learn a lot today, at least we learned a little, and if we didn't learn a little, at least we didn't get sick, and if we got sick, at least we didn't die; so, let us all be thankful."

LEO BUSCAGLIA, BORN FOR LOVE

The home environment and daily life are the themes in this chapter. Look out for the those things you tend to take for granted or that go unnoticed in your day and learn to appreciate them.

# HOME IS WHERE THE HEART IS

Draw your house and note all the details that make it special. Is it cosy and quiet or busy with people? Where is it located? Does it have great views or a fireplace, a porch, or deck outside?

NOTICE THE ROOFLINE –
IS IT MANSARD,
A-FRAME, GABLED, OR
FLAT? TILED, SHINGLE OR
THATCHED? WHAT KIND OF
PATTERN DOES IT MAKE?

WHAT SHAPE
AND STYLE ARE
YOUR DOOR AND
WINDOWS?

ADD DETAILS
THAT REFLECT
THE PEOPLE
WHO LIVE
INSIDE—MAYBE
A SURFBOARD,
SKIS, OR A
BICYCLE.

# A ROOM WITH A VIEW

Add your favorite piece of art to the blank wall or design
a wallpaper pattern you would love for your home.

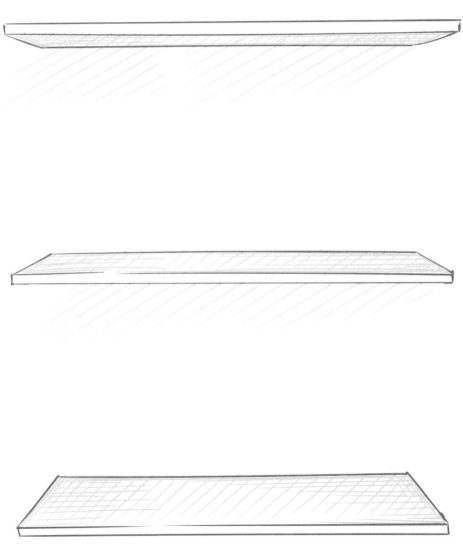

Draw your favorite objects to put on these shelves in your home.

# BRING NATURE INDOORS

Houseplants cheer up the home and remind us that there are always new beginnings blooming around us. Draw your growing plants and flowers in the pots. Include some new buds!

Color in these houseplants.

# YOUR DAILY BREW

Small things that brighten your day, like your first morning coffee or your favorite tea, can make all the difference to your sense of wellbeing. When you make your drink, take time to really savor the smell, temperature, and taste and notice the shape and feel of the cup.

Decorate the cups here with a pattern-draw your own mug if you like.

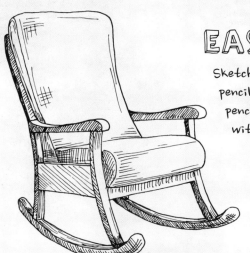

# EASY CHAIR

Sketch a line drawing of a chair in your home in pen or pencil, using cross-hatching, scribbles, stippling, or blended pencil to add shadows and depth and mark out features with texture, such as wood, metal, or upholstery.

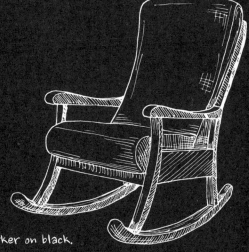

Then draw it using a white fine-tip pen or china marker on black.

# A BOUQUET FOR YOU

 Think about a time someone has brought you flowers or a time
you have given them as a gift. Draw the bouquet here.

Now try painting your flowers in different colorways: everything monochrome apart from the flowerheads, or color the flowers in unusual or unnatural shades.

# ON YOUR BIKE

How do you get around on your daily commute to work or school—by foot, bicycle, car, or train? Take a moment to appreciate the resources that get you from A to B. Draw your mode of transportation here—even if it's just your shoes. Use watercolors or brush pens to create lighter and darker areas of shading.

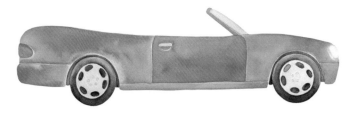

# FOUR OBJECTS

Choose four items you are grateful for that you use every day and draw them here in colored pen or pencil—they might be your toothbrush, a favorite mug or bowl, your headphones, your phone, or your water bottle.

# THE STREET YOU LIVE ON

Finish the street below, filling in all the little details—gates, fences, lampposts, postboxes, signs, and shop windows—that may have gone unnoticed.

# HYGGE
# HOME
# COMFORTS

The Danish use the word
"hygge" to describe the
things in your home
that give you feelings of
wellness and contentment.
What are yours? Color
these in and create
some of your own.

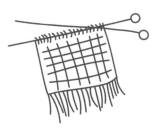

# A BIRD'S-EYE VIEW

Draw your house or office how you
imagine it would be from overhead –
as in the city intersection here.
Changing your view of something can
make you appreciate it more.

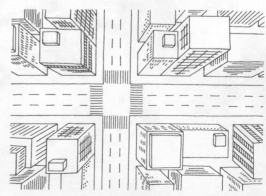

# SKYLINE SKETCHING

Draw a skyline of the city or town you live in, or a landscape of the country if that's where you live. When drawing outside, get the overall shapes down first, such as rooftops or the horizon line. You don't need to fill in all the details—focus on the specific features that grab your attention.

# FASHION ART

Certain items of clothing hold special memories, associations, or feelings.
Design a party outfit here—it may be an item that you love or has
special memories, or from your imagination.

Now design a pair of shoes—think about where those shoes might take you! Are they going to work or to exercise, to the beach, or are they slippers for staying at home?

# A GOOD NIGHT'S SLEEP

Sleep, rest, and relaxation are essential for good mental health and a positive outlook. Design your own pyjamas and sleep mask here to get you in the mood for rest.

# CITY STREET PATTERNS

When you are outside, take a look at the different paths you walk down. Where do you walk every day—is it on pavement, cobblestone, gravel, asphalt, or grass? Draw the patterns you notice. Here are some to start you off.

# A **DAY IN** **YOU**R **LIFE**

Track everything you did today in the squares on the opposite page, from waking up to going to sleep. They could include your morning croissant or pastry, a dog you encountered on the way to work, a newspaper or book you read, a yoga mat, a snack or lunch you particularly enjoyed, a flower you saw, or a glass of wine you had in the evening.

## Chapter 3:
# FAVORITE THINGS

"Gratitude unlocks the fullness of life. It turns what we have into enough, and more. It turns denial into acceptance, chaos to order, confusion to clarity. It can turn a meal into a feast, a house into a home, a stranger into a friend."

MELODY BEATTIE

Explore your most-loved objects, activities, places, and food here—you may realize that even the memory of these can lift your mood and bring you joy. Paying attention to the emotions, sensations, textures, and colors that you associate with your favorite things can make you appreciate them more and enhance your artistic work.

# HAPPY COLORS

What colors do you associate with happiness? With peace? Or calm? Sketch line drawings of items you link with the mood of the colors here, such as the dove on blue. Write down how the colors make you feel.

# SCENT MEMORY

Think about a favorite fragrance memory, such as your grandmother's perfume, fir trees in a forest, or baking bread. When you draw it, try to capture all sense associations—what the aroma would look like, its weight and substance, how it would feel if it had texture. For example, your granny's perfume might evoke a delicate wash of blue or purple, whereas freshly baked bread might naturally feel like a dense and earthy brown.

# YOUR FAVORITE COLOR

Fill the space with things that are in your favorite color.

# FRUIT SHAPES

Draw a pencil still life of one of your favorite fruits—
like these pears here. Note their varying shades and
pitting. Then color in your shading with watercolors
or markers, leaving patches of white paper for
highlights and the lightest areas.

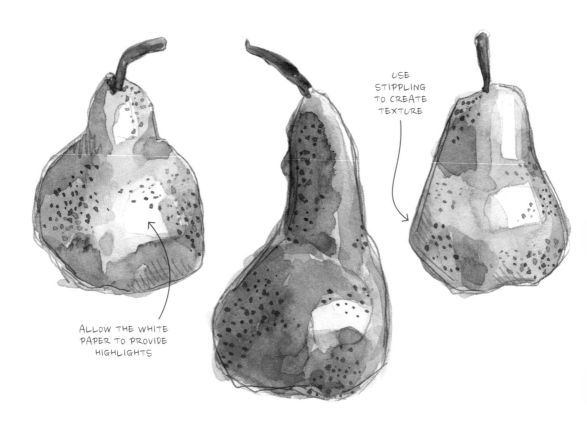

USE
STIPPLING
TO CREATE
TEXTURE

ALLOW THE WHITE
PAPER TO PROVIDE
HIGHLIGHTS

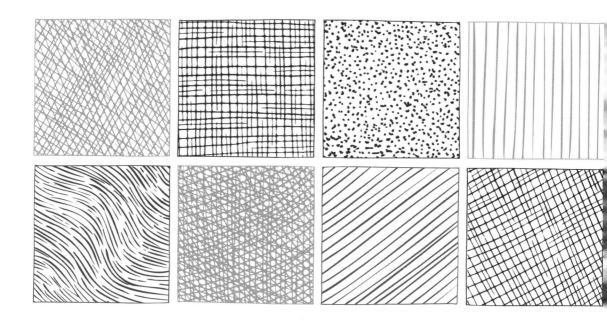

# MARK-MAKING TECHNIQUES

Experiment with mark-making techniques. Try crosshatching, parallel lines, dots, strokes, ticks, and squiggles. Use lead or colored pencil, fine-tip pen or markers for different effects.

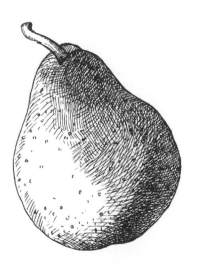

Now try a pen-and-ink
fruit drawing using just
crosshatching techniques.

# MUSIC TIME

What is your favorite instrument? What is it about the sound it makes that you love? Color in these and draw your own.

Fill in the rest of this page with musical notes
in different colors, sizes, and thicknesses,
overlapping some notes with others.
Write in the lyrics of your
favorite song.

# A GIFT FOR YOU

What is the best gift you were ever given?
Color in the wrapping on these presents.

Color in this geometric repeat pattern to design your own giftwrap.
Try using a gold or silver metallic pen for one detail.

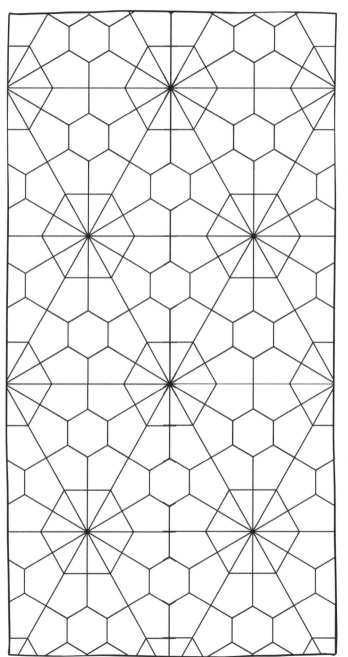

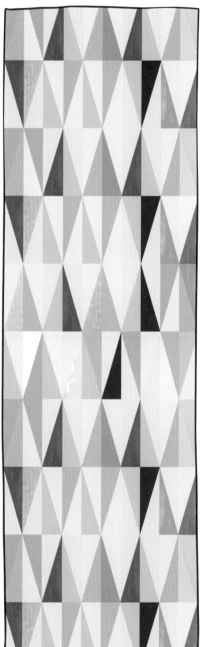

# A TIME FOR EVERY SEASON

Draw a different scene for each season in the squares below—include details of the weather, changing landscapes, and animal life. Which is your favorite season? Is there something to love even about the one you enjoy the least?

WINTER

SPRING

SUMMER

FALL

# A MERRY CHRISTMAS

Everyone loves this holiday—it brings happiness to all. Draw something that reminds you of this joyous festive season, such as filled stockings, mistletoe, a Christmas tree, or snowman.

# POINTILLISM STILL LIFE

Still lives are usually household objects, fruit, or flowers. Choose a selection of favorite objects in your home or your favorite flower, then use the pointillism technique of rendering it in small dots.

LAYER DIFFERENT COLORS OF DOTS

SPACE SOME DOTS FAR APART AND OTHERS CLOSE TOGETHER TO CREATE SHADING

# MONEY CAN'T BUY ME...

Write down everything that you are grateful for that is free. Use a variety of font styles and mix up lowercase and uppercase.

# FAVORITE ACTIVITY

What do you love to do best in your free time? Yoga, running, tennis, reading a book, painting, knitting? Draw it here.

# IT'S ALL ENTERTAINMENT

Draw something here that entertains you—it might be an image from your favorite cartoon, movie, TV show, or book.

# STOP AND SMELL THE ROSES

What simple thing brought you pleasure today? Draw it here.

# COSY FIRES

There's nothing cosier than a warm fire when it's cold and snowy outside. Draw the room around this fireplace and include a window with snow falling outside.

# KEEP WARM WITH MITTENS

Design patterns on these mittens, following the weft-and-warp weave or intarsia of real knitting patterns. You could try Fair Isle, stripes or chevrons, or winter motifs such as snowflakes, hearts, or Christmas trees.

# DELICIOUS DINING

Whether it is pizza, noodles, lobster, or chocolate cake, food keeps you nourished and happy. Draw your favorite food here.

Now draw the cutlery you need to eat it. Ornate silver
knife and fork, chopsticks, plastic spoon?

# YOUR HAPPY PLACE

What place in the whole world do you love the most? It could be an exotic foreign city or beach, or just a room in your home. Travel to your special place and draw the landscape here.

# HOLIDAY MEMORIES

Pick out one image or landmark that reminds you of a wonderful holiday and draw it here.

Chapter 4:

# NATURE & ANIMALS

"There are only two ways to live your life. One is as though nothing is a miracle. The other is as though everything is a miracle."

ALBERT EINSTEIN

Expressing gratitude for the gifts we receive from the natural world—the Earth and sun, plants and wildlife—reawakens our connection to nature. Take some time to go outside and notice the world around you, from a tiny insect under a rock to a panoramic landscape. Draw what you see!

# DEAR WORLD...

Write a thank-you letter to the planet, listing all it provides for your sustenance: water, fresh produce, oxygen to breathe. Design the letterhead, envelope, and the stamp too.

# THE LONELY PLANET

We often think of our planet floating alone in a dark universe, but we live in a complex and beautiful solar system in space. Draw the universe as you see it around planet Earth.

# HUG A TREE

On your next walk in nature, keep a lookout for a tree you like. You don't have to hug it, but do take a moment to remind yourself of its contribution to the planet and wonder at its longevity and resilience. Take a photo of it, and re-draw it here.

# TREE SHAPES

There's a remarkable variety of tree shapes. Instead of starting with the trunk, paint some blobs in different shapes and colors and add the trunk and branches afterwards. Try a columnar shape for a juniper or poplar, conical for a fir tree, a spreading shape for a cherry or a round one for a maple or pear.

# BARK

Try out different bark textures on these tree trunks below. For example, white birch has horizontal fine lines with peeling strips, beech is smooth and oak and ash have deep vertical ridges. Here's where mark-making techniques (see page 70) will come in handy for pen and pencil, or use watercolor or crayon if you prefer.

# THROUGH THE SEASONS

Add leaves, blossom or fruit to these branches. Add grass, leafy ground, or mossy earth, depending on your terrain and the season. Add mountains or a river.

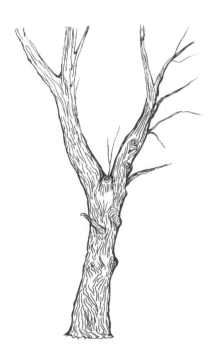

# LEAVES

Collect leaves on your next nature walk, and recreate them here—try to collect as many different kinds as you can to really appreciate their shapes and markings, such as maple, oak, rowan, poplar, chestnut, and birch.

# FEATHERS

Collect feathers, too, and draw yours here.

97

# VEGETABLE GARDEN

Continue the line drawings to plant more vegetables in the garden.

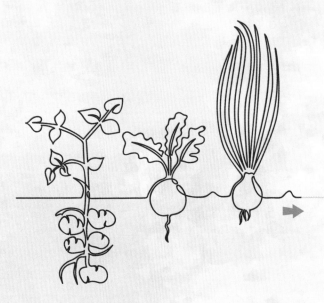

# FLOWER GARLAND

Finish the flower wreath here,
filling it in and adding other types
of flowers and foliage if you like.

# BLUE SKIES ABOVE

Add more clouds and fill in a blue sky. Add a sun peeking behind a cloud.
Alternatively, color the sky violet or orange and make the clouds gray.

Create three more skies here, like this sunset: try a sunrise over a mountain, a night sky, and a stormy sky.

# RAINFOREST

The world is filled with variety and color. Color in this rainforest scene.

# A HIKING TRAIL

Fill in the details of what you notice on your nature hike—add in more trees and rocks, texture for the mountain and color in the sky. Do you see campers? Draw them in.

# A NIGHT SKY

Using a white pen, fill this black page with more shooting stars, planets, moons, and constellations.

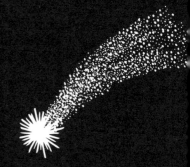

Now doodle as many different styles of stars as you can using various colors, sizes, and points.

105

# SNOW DAYS AND RAINY DAYS

Skiing, ice-skating and snowball fights are just some of the wonderful ways to enjoy winter snow. Draw a happy memory of snow.

Draw snowflake designs here.

Keep the rain off with your umbrella –
something to be thankful for on a wet day!
Decorate yours in cheery designs.

# RAINBOWS

Into life some rain must fall, but there are always rainbows.
Fill the sky with raindrops (they don't have to be gray).

Now fill the page with rainbows. Use thick and thin lines, blend colors and decorate them with patterns, dots, and stripes. Experiment with mediums too—pastels give a soft diffused edge.

SILLY

warm & fluffy

CURIOUS

# PET LOVE

What is it about your pet that makes you grateful for its company?
Draw your pet and name its characteristics. If you don't have a pet,
think about one you had as a child or one you would like to have.

happy to see me

FUNNY FACE

Color in these pets and add details such as stripes, spots, or splodges.

# BIRD LIFE

Take a moment to really look at the birds that visit your garden, or that you see in a park, or on the street. Study their movements and listen to their chirps and tweets. Notice the texture of their feathers and their markings. Draw one you see on the branch of a tree, on a birdfeeder, or in a birdhouse.

# BUTTERFLY PATTERNS

Marvel at nature's designs in the beautiful patterns and wing shapes of these butterflies. Take them as inspiration and draw your own, using colored markers, pens, pencils, or paints.

# SEA CREATURES

The ocean covers more than 70 percent of the surface of the Earth and is home to richly diverse inhabitants. Celebrate sealife by drawing beautiful and exotic sea creatures like these.

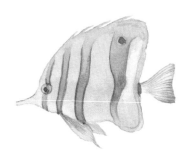

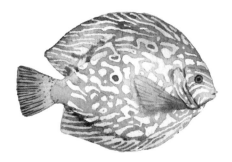

# BEACHCOMBING

There's a treasure of natural gifts just lying on the shoreline. If you have a shell you've picked up from summer holidays that brings back good memories, draw it here. Use pencils or crayons to create soft pearlescent colors.

# BEE HAPPY FOR BEES

The world's most important pollinators, bees are vital to a healthy ecosystem and environment. Draw bees swarming back to their hive where they will make honey for you to enjoy.

# SPIDEY SENSE

This is one creepy crawly that we want around. Spiders feast on pesky insects such as fleas, aphids, and caterpillars, helping to stop the spread of diseases to plant crops. Have some fun drawing their lanky legs and include their web.

Feel the Universe inside of you

## Chapter 5:

# BODY & SELF

"Be thankful for what you have; you'll end up having more. If you concentrate on what you don't have, you will never, ever have enough."

OPRAH WINFREY

The drawing prompts and activities in this chapter are designed to encourage self-reflection and positivity. They will help you recognize all the talents, traits, skills, and attributes that make you special, and help you become aware of your physical body and all the miraculous things it can do.

# BODY POSITIVE

Name four things you like about your physical body and draw them here. You might like that you are tall and have long legs, which means you can reach high shelves or run fast. Perhaps you like your freckles, the color of your eyes or the way your hair turns blond in the sun. Rejoice in the physical details that make you you.

# SKILLS AND TALENTS

Now name and draw four skills and talents—sports, artistic, academic ––that you have and take a moment to be proud of all that you can do.

# CREATIVE EXPRESSION

Pens, pencils and markers help
us communicate and express ourselves.
Draw one of your favorite mark-making
tools or color in the pens here.

OFFICE

OFFICE

PEN

How do you use color in your creative work? Create a picture using each of the colors here.

# NEGATIVE SPACE

Instead of drawing your body, color in the space around it to make a negative-space image. You might want to refer to a photograph before you begin. Avoid sketching in an outline, just start coloring in the background in any shade you like.

# SILHOUETTES

Now create a body shape in a traditional silhouette, but fill the shape with encouraging words that support self-belief. You might choose "I am beautiful," "I am strong," "I believe in me," or "I am an essential part of the world."

# HAPPY
# THOUGHTS

What makes you laugh, fills
you with joy, or lifts you up?
Write the words in these balloons
and color them in or draw faces
and smiles on the balloons.

# YOUR SUNNY SIDE

What kind or positive words has someone said about you, and how would you describe yourself? Fill the suns with self-affirming words and draw some more of your own.

# THANKSGIVING MANDALA

What centers you and makes you feel happy and well? Can you bring more of this into your life every day? Draw more outer circles on these mandalas, recording a thanksgiving that contributes to your wellbeing within each.

# ZENTANGLE THERAPY

To slow down, and enhance relaxation and focus, finish the zentangle here,
simply building on the design. Before you start, take a moment to be mindful
and appreciate your coloring tools and this activity.

# LIFE DRAWINGS

Your body is equipped with powerful tools to experience the world—delight in them here! Using pencil or pen and ink, draw some eyes.

Your mouth enables you to talk, sing, shout, whistle—how amazing is that! Draw mouths here.

Ears allow you to hear people, animals and all sorts of noises, including your favorite music. Draw a few here.

Your hands serve you every day in so many ways, with daily tasks as well as caring touches. Draw your own hand here.

# SILENCE AND BREATH

Many people take time to be thankful during a moment of silence, whether that is a prayer before a meal or during meditation. Take time here to breathe deeply, embrace the quiet, and give thanks. Reflect on what silence might look like—plumes of blue smoke, starry space, a white whisper of a cloud—and draw yourself in the moment with silence all around you.

# BE THANKFUL FOR A REST

What are the ways in which you relax, recuperate, and turn off from your busy day? Is it a deep sleep, a good book, some chilled music? Draw your favorite ways to relax here.

# THE DIVINE FEMININE

Tap into your inner goddess by drawing wild hair styles, flower and fruit headdresses, crowns, or tiaras on this figure. Change her skin tone and coloring. Make her shamanic or wiccan, Norse or Navajo, Indian or Egyptian.

Chapter 6:

# DREAMS & CELEBRATIONS

"Today I choose to live with gratitude for the love that fills my heart, the peace that rests within my spirit and the voice of hope that says all things are possible."

ANONYMOUS

Celebrate your goals, dreams, and achievements on the following pages. Not only do these drawing prompts take a look back at what you've already achieved, but they also look at those things you have cause to celebrate now as well as the promise of the future.

# GIVE **YOUR**SELF AN AWARD

You've won a trophy! What is it for? It could be a simple act of kindness to another, a small win at work, a personal best, or a career promotion or an academic degree. Design and date it.

What are your good deeds? Give yourself rosettes and medals for these too, and create a few for your friends, colleagues, and family members.

# DREAMCATCHERS

Draw a dreamcatcher to identify your still unfulfilled dreams for something you've always wanted to do or become. Think about your dreams from childhood and whether they are still with you.

# CHINESE LANTERNS

Traditionally released to celebrate the Chinese New Year and bestow good wishes for a long, healthy, and peaceful life, these lanterns are constructed from bamboo or wire with a paper or silk shade. Draw yours here, hanging on a tree, floating on water or drifting into the sky.

# SIMPLE THINGS TO CELEBRATE

Be grateful for the small stuff – a birthday remembered, a chat with a friend, a card that came in the post, a woolly hat on a cold day – and list or draw a few of them here. Make the words or images in miniature on the page to remind yourself that the best things come in small packages.

# GUILTY PLEASURES

Delight in any small or big luxury—a sweet treat like chocolate or macaroons, a glass of wine, binge-watching TV, takeaway food, a weekly manicure. Draw your top guilty pleasures here.

# PARTY PLANNING

If you were planning a party, what would you celebrate? Make streamers and bunting for hanging. Use stripes, chequerboard, polka dot, or floral patterns, or coordinate to your party theme.

Who is the cake for? Is it to celebrate a wedding or birthday? Design your cake.

# OPEN DOORS

People will open doors for you in life. Reflect on those mentors, teachers, or individuals who helped you on your way. Draw a picture of your future in the open door, then create some doors in different styles to remind you to pass opportunities on to others.

# THREE KEYS

Now draw some keys to doors—what are your three keys
to success, or your three keys to happiness?

# SHADOWS

There is no light without shadow.
Draw a few objects with shadows
in lead or colored pencil, like
the sketches of fruit here.

# SILVER LININGS

Reflect on a particularly difficult challenge that made you learn something about yourself—a cloud that had a silver lining. Use a silver pen to draw the silver lining on your clouds.

SIGNPOSTS

Reflect on the events, situations, or people that served as signposts at forks in the road through the journey of your life. What would the signs say? Copy retro sign designs or woodcut, chalkboard, script lettering, or shouty capital letters.

Now draw signs to point you forward into the future—what do these say?

Now draw some other objects that show directions, such as a compass, weathervane, or windsock.

# PICTURE FRAME

Recollect a happy memory and draw it in the frame.

# A MOUNTAIN CLIMBED

Everyone has faced a challenge or goal they weren't sure they could meet. Take a moment to be grateful for the mountains (or foothills) you had to climb and those still in front of you. Draw a few here in different styles.

# LIGHT BULB MOMENTS

Think about an occasion when you had a "Eureka" moment. Draw a few lightbulbs in different styles here. Remember to treasure those flashes of inspiration when they come again in the future.

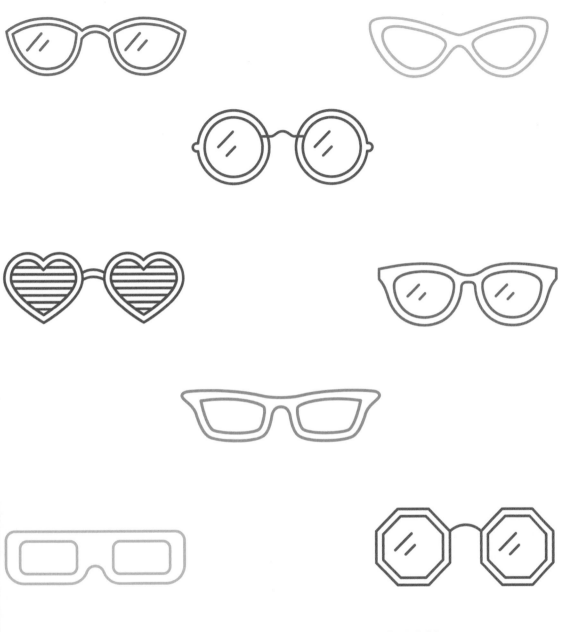

# THE FUTURE IS BRIGHT

You'll need your sunglasses! Color these in different patterns and create some designs of your own—don't be afraid to make them as wacky and outrageous as you can.

# HOPE POSTCARD

Design a postcard centered around Emily Dickinson's poem
"Hope is a thing with feathers, that perches in the soul."

# THE REVERSE BUCKET LIST

Make a list of some of your previous achievements and draw some of them here. They could be an engagement or wedding, foreign travel, a bungee or parachute jump.

# DESTINATION DREAM

If you could go anywhere in the world, where would you go? Design a hot-air balloon to take you there.

Color in these
hot-air balloons
with crayons, colored
pencils, felt-tip
or brush pens.